Written by
Cheryl Apgar

Editor: Sheri Samoiloff
Illustrator: Darcy Tom
Cover Photographer: Michael Jarrett
Cover Illustrator: Kim Graves
Designer: Corina Chien
Cover Designer: Corina Chien
Art Director: Tom Cochrane
Project Director: Carolea Williams

© 2002 Creative Teaching Press, Inc., Huntington Beach, CA 92649
Reproduction of activities in any manner for use in the classroom and not for commercial sale is permissible.
Reproduction of these materials for an entire school or for a school system is strictly prohibited.

Table of Contents

Introduction

Layer It! With Science brings the love of reading and science into the early-childhood classroom. This innovative resource shows you how to help each child in your class create thematic, interactive, rhyming layer books for a variety of physical science, life science, and earth science topics. Children will create books about animals, weather, land formations, matter, habitats, and more. Easy-to-follow directions, lively illustrations, and moveable art pieces make these books fun for teachers and children alike!

A child's language skills develop quickly during the early-childhood years. Children develop their listening skills, increase their vocabulary, and begin to make the transition from oral to written language. *Layer It! With Science* provides the materials for reinforcing these skills. Children practice their fine motor skills as they color, cut out, and organize their very own layer books. The completed books become great tools for shared and independent reading and enhance any science unit.

Children can construct these layer books with minimal or no help from an adult, making them a great tool for building a child's independence and self-esteem. Very little teacher preparation is involved, and all suggested materials can be substituted with other materials. In addition, each layer book includes a writing prompt to help children explore the connections between the theme of study and their own life.

Each layer of these adorable, hands-on books brings a year's worth of opportunities for children to grow as readers, writers, speakers, and listeners!

Making a Layer Book

The construction of each layer book is a progressive, week-long activity. Children complete one page each day, allowing for daily review of concepts and reinforcement of targeted skills. (See the activity ideas on pages 6–8.) Essentially, each layer book is a theme-related poem with corresponding art pieces that children color, cut out, and glue on the four or five pages of the book.

Each layer book includes a directions page(s) that includes a materials list and a detailed explanation of how to create each layer book page; a reproducible page of art pieces; and four or five reproducible layer book pages. Follow these step-by-step directions to guide children through the creation of each layer book:

1. Write each child's name on a separate file folder. Have children title their folder *Layer Books in Progress*.

2. Copy all the reproducibles shown in the materials list on 9" x 12" (23 cm x 30.5 cm) pieces of construction paper. Use the recommended colors listed in the materials list, or select your own colors.

3. Give each child the reproducible page of art pieces and an envelope. Have children color and cut out the art pieces and then store them in their envelope. Ask children to write their name on their envelope. Have them place their envelope in their file folder.

4. Decide whether you want children to assemble each book from front to back or back to front. If children start with page 1, they will read each line of the poem as they assemble their book. If they start with the last page of the poem, they can easily stack their completed pages in the correct order. Choose the method that works best with your class.

5. At the beginning of each day's activity, give children their file folder, a reproducible page, and the necessary art materials for that page. Use the directions page(s) to show children how to cut off the diamond pattern on the reproducible, how to color and/or use art materials to decorate the remainder of the page, and where to glue each art piece. At the end of each day's activity, have children place their envelope and their completed page in their folder. Collect the folders.

6. You will need to cut a slit in one or more pages of each layer book. The directions page(s) indicate exactly where to make each slit. Use an X-ACTO® knife or a sharp pair of scissors to cut the slit in each child's copy of the page before he or she works with it. Never allow children to handle X-ACTO® knives or sharp scissors.

7. Children will need at least one craft stick for most of the layer books. Cut craft sticks as needed to fit a page. For example, if the directions call for a craft stick to be used on page 1 or 2 of a book, cut the sticks to make them shorter (so that they do not obstruct pages 3, 4, and 5). Have children glue the center of the art piece on the stick in a horizontal or vertical direction depending on the page setup. You can substitute straws, coffee stirrers, cut index cards, or other sturdy items for craft sticks.

8. Once children have completed all the pages of their book, make sure their pages are in sequential order. Staple together the completed books, and have a reading celebration.

9. Invite children to read their completed book in a whole-class setting or during guided reading, partner reading, or independent reading. Have them read their book chorally, or assign each child a page to read for a reader's theater.

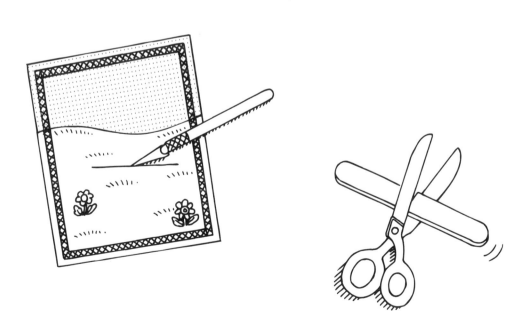

Skill Building

Before the class begins to assemble a layer book, use the ideas in this section to introduce the theme and prepare children to read the text. Then, after children have assembled and explored their book, choose one of the assessment tools to determine their mastery of reading and writing skills. Choose additional skill-building activities that complement your unit of study. All activities are flexible, and you can alter the directions to fit the needs of your class.

Before You Begin

Before you introduce a layer book, ask children to share what they know about the theme. Write children's ideas on a piece of chart paper, and display it on a board or wall.

Introducing the Theme

Use the following ideas to introduce the theme of study:

• Read aloud books about the theme.

• Have children make murals about the theme. Label the items in the murals that relate to the theme.

• Make a thematic word wall or class dictionary of thematic terms.

• Write thematic words on die-cut shapes or stationery, and display them around the room.

Presenting the Layer Book

Each time you select a layer book for children to complete, use the following activities throughout the week to teach new concepts and reinforce skills. Introduce one or two skills each day.

Analyze This ●

Write the poem from the chosen layer book on a large piece of chart paper or sentence strips. Display the chart paper, or place the sentence strips in a pocket chart. Use a different color ink for each line of the poem. As an option, laminate the chart paper so you can write on it with overhead transparency markers. Use a wet paper towel to wipe off the ink at the end of each activity.

- Introduce the selected poem by asking children to read it (as they are able) and look for familiar words. Engage children in conversation about the subject to assess their prior knowledge and to introduce the concept.

- Point to each word, and have children echo each line of the poem as you read it. Emphasize rhyming words by underlining each rime on the chart.

- Say or sing the poem as you point to the words on the chart. Invite volunteers to point to the words on the chart while the rest of the class reads along.

- Have children search for capital letters. Invite children to circle each capital letter.

- Have children search for punctuation marks. Invite children to draw a triangle around each punctuation mark. Discuss the name of each mark.

- Invite children to identify and spell all the rhyming words.

- Challenge advanced children to use the rimes to make a list of other rhyming words and then substitute the new words to make a nonsense poem.

- Invite children to use simple instruments or jump ropes as they sing or chant the poem.

- Write five high-frequency words on the chalkboard. Have children search through their completed layer book to see how many of the high-frequency words from the board are also in their book. As a class, read the high-frequency words found in the layer book.

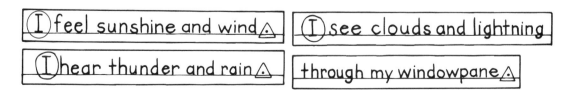

Extension Activities

Use the following activities to have children practice their listening skills, locate punctuation marks, review parts of speech, learn rhyming words, and practice letter recognition.

Are You Listening? •

Alter the sentences to fit each layer book. Have children set their completed book in front of them before you begin. Slowly read aloud the directions, and pause after each direction.

1. Point to the_____ on page _____ of your book.
2. Find the object in your book that you can slide. Whisper the name of the object.
3. Draw a _____ on page 4.
4. Count the number of feet you can find in your book.
5. Count the number of eyes you can find in your book.
6. Find your favorite page. Draw a happy face on the back of the page.
7. Find the last page in your book. Read that page silently.
8. Count the number of capital letters in your book. Hold up the same number of fingers as your answer.
9. Lift the flap on page _____. What do you see? Stand up if you see an animal.
10. Are there two or more children in your book? If yes, raise your index finger.

Assess children's listening skills by observing their actions, their interactions with others, and their answers.

Show Me •

Begin by writing the poem on a piece of chart paper, or have children follow along in their completed layer book. Customize the directions to correspond to the poem in each layer book.

Ask children to place their index finger on the following:
- a specific capital letter
- a vowel
- a consonant
- a word that begins with the same letter as the first letter in their first name
- a word that ends with the same letter as the first letter in their last name
- a word that rhymes with _____

Farm Fun

Materials

- ✂ Art Pieces reproducible (page 10) white
- ✂ Page One reproducible (page 11) green
- ✂ Page Two reproducible (page 12) yellow
- ✂ Page Three reproducible (page 13) red
- ✂ Page Four reproducible (page 14) blue
- ✂ crayons or markers
- ✂ scissors
- ✂ glue
- ✂ X-ACTO® knife (optional) (for teacher use only)
- ✂ craft sticks
- ✂ cotton balls

Directions •

Art Pieces Give each child an Art Pieces reproducible and an envelope. Have children color and cut out the eight art pieces and place them inside their envelope. Tell children to place their envelope in their file folder. Collect each child's folder, and distribute it at the beginning of each day's activity.

Page One Give each child a Page One reproducible. Have children remove the pig and the haystack art pieces from their envelope. Tell children to cut off the diamond pattern on the page and discard it. Ask them to color the remainder of the page and glue the pig over the letter A and the top edge of the haystack over the letter B.

Page Two Give each child a Page Two reproducible. Have children remove the hen and cover art pieces from their envelope. Tell children to cut off the diamond pattern on the page and discard it. Ask them to color the remainder of the page and glue the hen over the letter C. Have children glue the top edge of the cover over the letter D (along the top edge of the hen coop).

Page Three Cut a slit next to the letter E on each child's Page Three reproducible. Give children their revised page, a craft stick, and one cotton ball. Have them remove the sheep art piece from their envelope, glue it to the craft stick, and glue the cotton ball on the sheep. Set aside the art pieces until the glue is dry. Tell children to cut off the diamond pattern on the page and discard it. Ask them to color the remainder of the page and then slide the prepared craft stick through the slit.

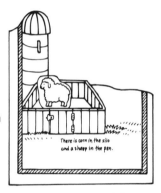

Page Four Give each child a Page Four reproducible. Have children remove the cow, horse, and barn door art pieces from their envelope. Ask children to color the page and glue the cow over the letter F and the horse over the letter G. Have them glue the left edge of the barn door over the letter H (along the left edge of the doorway). Invite children to respond to the writing prompt.

Art Pieces

A

B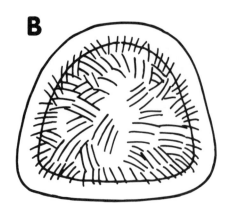

C

D

E

G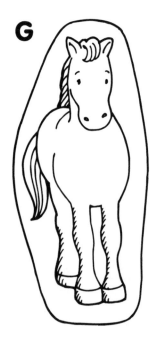

F

H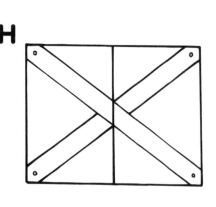

Layer It! With Science © 2002 Creative Teaching Press

There is a pig in the sty.

1

Layer It! With Science © 2002 Creative Teaching Press

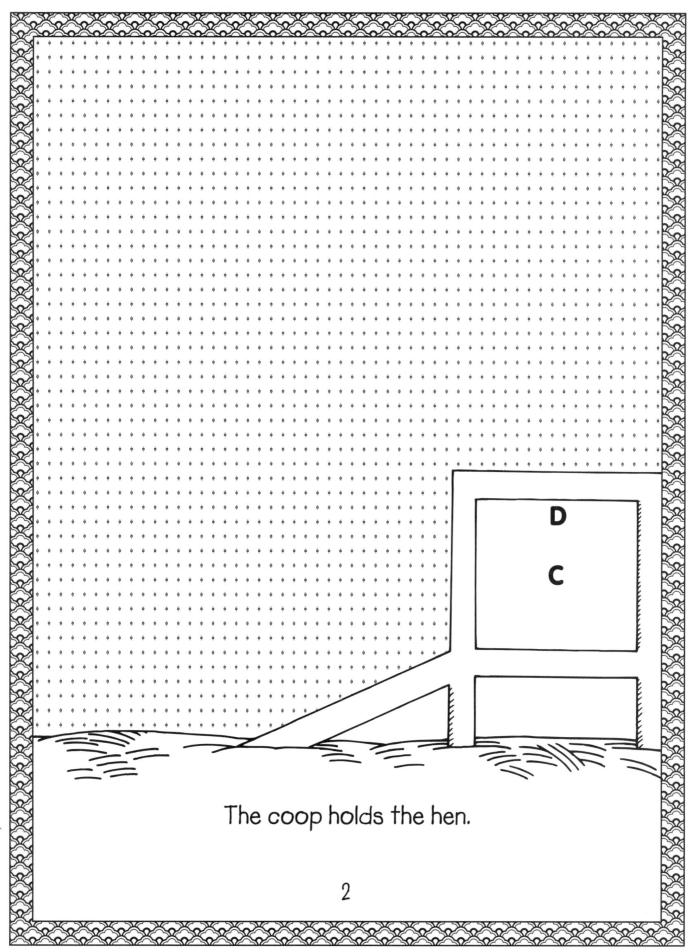

The coop holds the hen.

2

Layer It! With Science © 2002 Creative Teaching Press

There is corn in the silo
and a sheep in the pen.

3

Layer It! With Science © 2002 Creative Teaching Press

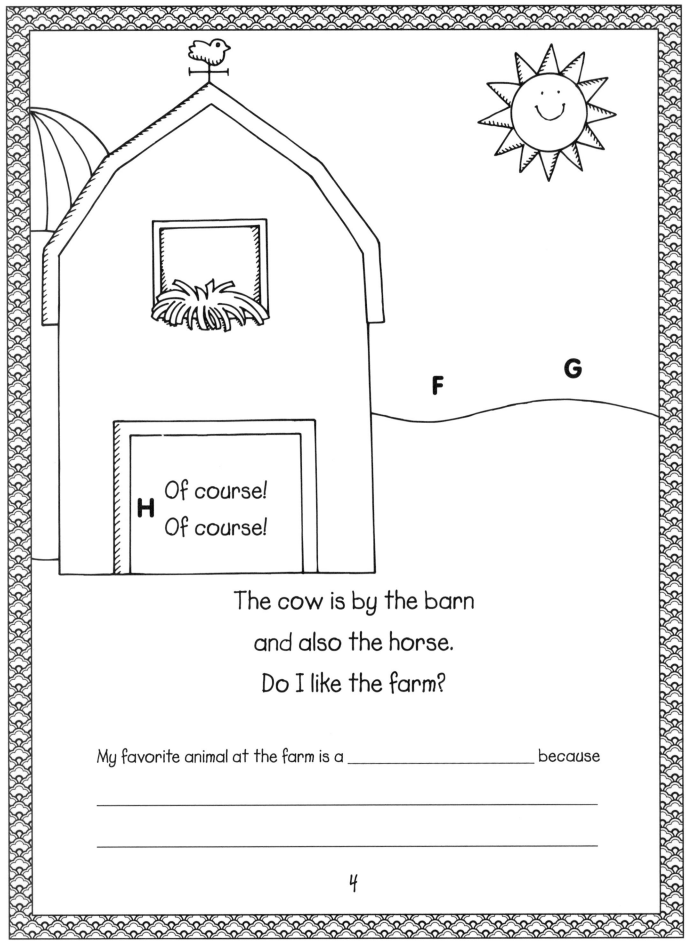

F   G

H   Of course!
Of course!

The cow is by the barn

and also the horse.

Do I like the farm?

My favorite animal at the farm is a _____ because

_____

_____

4

Layer It! With Science © 2002 Creative Teaching Press

From Egg to Chicken

Materials

- ✂ Art Pieces reproducible (page 17) white
- ✂ Page One reproducible (page 18) beige or cream
- ✂ Page Two reproducible (page 19) light brown
- ✂ Page Three reproducible (page 20) light green
- ✂ Page Four reproducible (page 21) light blue
- ✂ Page Five reproducible (page 22) white
- ✂ crayons or markers
- ✂ scissors
- ✂ glue
- ✂ X-ACTO® knife (optional) (for teacher use only)
- ✂ craft sticks
- ✂ brass fasteners

Directions ●

Art Pieces Give each child an Art Pieces reproducible and an envelope. Have children color and cut out the five art pieces and place them inside their envelope. Tell children to place their envelope in their file folder. Collect each child's folder, and distribute it at the beginning of each day's activity.

Page Two Give each child a Page Two reproducible. Tell children to cut off the diamond pattern on the page and discard it. Ask them to color the remainder of the page.

Page One Give each child a Page One reproducible. Have children remove the egg art piece from their envelope. Tell children to cut off the diamond pattern on the page and discard it. Ask them to color the remainder of the page and then glue the top edge of the egg over the letter A (along the top edge of the inside of the egg).

Page Three Cut a slit next to the letter B on each child's Page Three reproducible. Give children their revised page and a craft stick. Have children remove the chick art piece from their envelope and glue it to the craft stick. Tell them to cut off the diamond pattern on the page and discard it. Ask children to color the remainder of the page and then slide the prepared craft stick through the slit.

Page Four Give each child a Page Four reproducible. Have children remove the hen and rooster art pieces from their envelope. Tell children to cut off the diamond pattern on the page and discard it. Ask them to color the remainder of the page and glue the hen over the letter C and the rooster over the letter D.

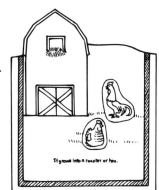

Page Five Give each child a Page Five reproducible and a brass fastener. Have children remove the life cycle art piece from their envelope. Ask children to color the page and place the brass fastener through the dot on the life cycle and the dot on the page (below the letter E). Invite them to turn the life cycle in the direction of the arrows to learn about the life cycle of the chicken and then respond to the writing prompt.

Art Pieces

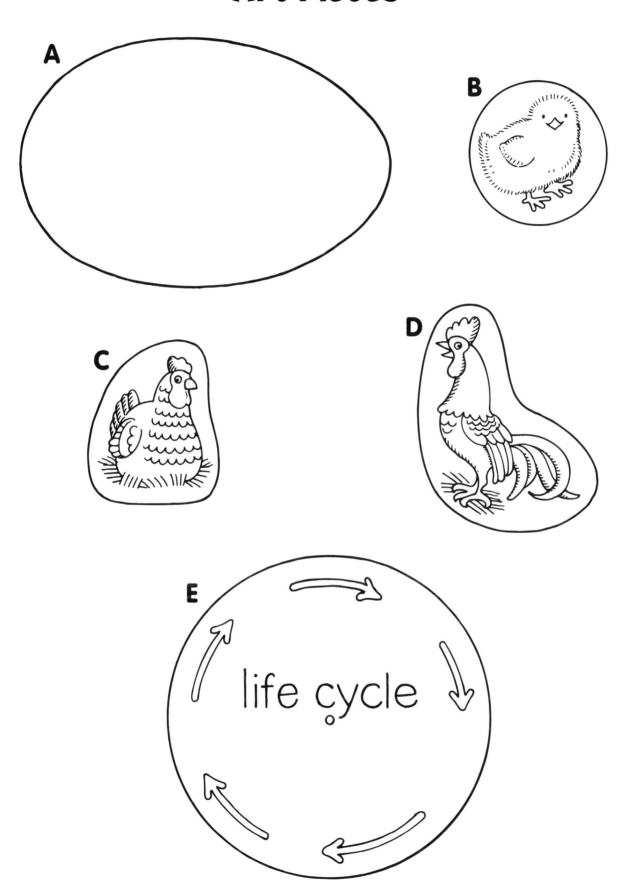

A

B

C

D

E life cycle

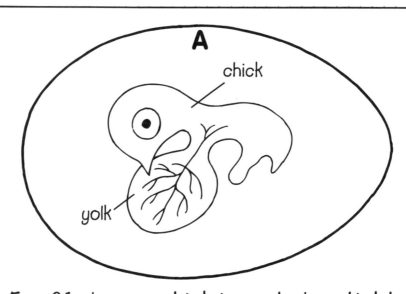

For 21 days, a chick is curled up tight
inside the egg where it's dark day and night.

1

Layer It! With Science © 2002 Creative Teaching Press

But then the chick starts to peck at the shell.

Soon it will be out, and all will be well.

2

Layer It! With Science © 2002 Creative Teaching Press

B —————————————

The baby chick eats and sleeps,
and then . . .

3

Layer It! With Science © 2002 Creative Teaching Press

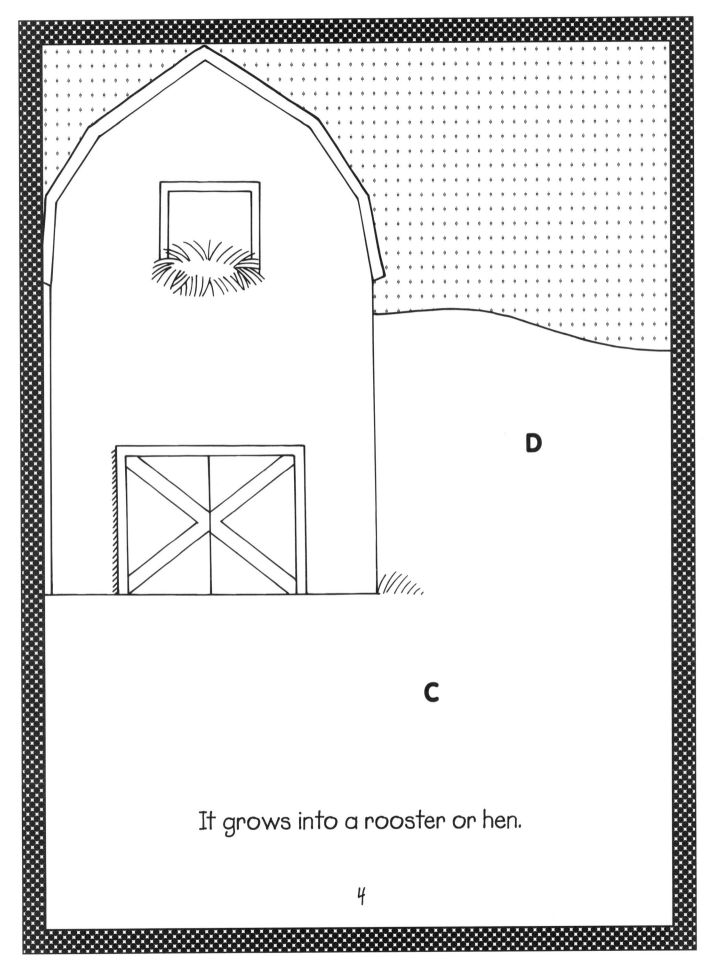

D

C

It grows into a rooster or hen.

4

Layer It! With Science © 2002 Creative Teaching Press

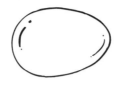

E
•

Now a hen lays an egg, and what do you know?

Around again the life cycle will go.

List the stages of the chicken's life. _____

_____

_____

5

Layer It! With Science © 2002 Creative Teaching Press

Land Formations

Materials

- ✂ Art Pieces reproducible (page 24)
- ✂ Page One reproducible (page 25) light blue
- ✂ Page Two reproducible (page 26) tan
- ✂ Page Three reproducible (page 27) light green
- ✂ Page Four reproducible (page 28) white
- ✂ crayons or markers
- ✂ scissors
- ✂ glue
- ✂ X-ACTO® knife (optional) (for teacher use only)
- ✂ craft sticks
- ✂ translucent glitter
- ✂ cotton balls

Directions ●

Art Pieces
Give each child an Art Pieces reproducible and an envelope. Have children color and cut out the four art pieces and place them inside their envelope. Tell children to place their envelope in their file folder. Collect each child's folder, and distribute it at the beginning of each day's activity.

Page One
Give each child a Page One reproducible. Tell children to cut off the diamond pattern on the page and discard it. Ask them to color the remainder of the page.

Page Two
Give each child a Page Two reproducible. Have children remove the cactus art piece from their envelope. Tell children to cut off the diamond pattern on the page and discard it. Ask them to color the remainder of the page and glue the cactus over the letter A.

Page Three
Cut a slit next to the letter B on each child's Page Three reproducible. Give children their revised page and a craft stick. Have them remove the squirrels and horse art pieces from their envelope and glue the squirrels to the craft stick. Tell children to cut off the diamond pattern on the page and discard it. Ask them to color the remainder of the page, glue the horse over the letter C, and slide the prepared craft stick through the slit.

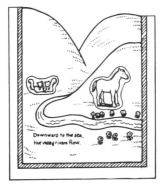

Page Four
Give each child a Page Four reproducible, translucent glitter, and one cotton ball. Have children remove the clouds art piece from their envelope. Have children tear their cotton ball into small pieces and glue the pieces over the clouds. Set aside the art pieces until the glue is dry. Invite children to respond to the writing prompt. Ask them to color the page, glue glitter on the top edge of the mountains to resemble snow, and glue the clouds over the letter D. Set aside the pages until the glue is dry.

Art Pieces

A
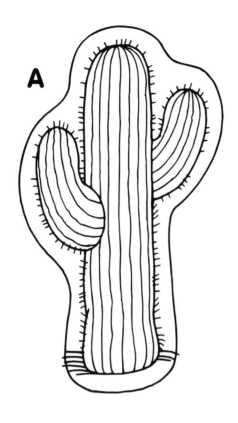

B

D

C

Layer It! With Science © 2002 Creative Teaching Press

Water surrounds an island on every side.

1

Layer It! With Science © 2002 Creative Teaching Press

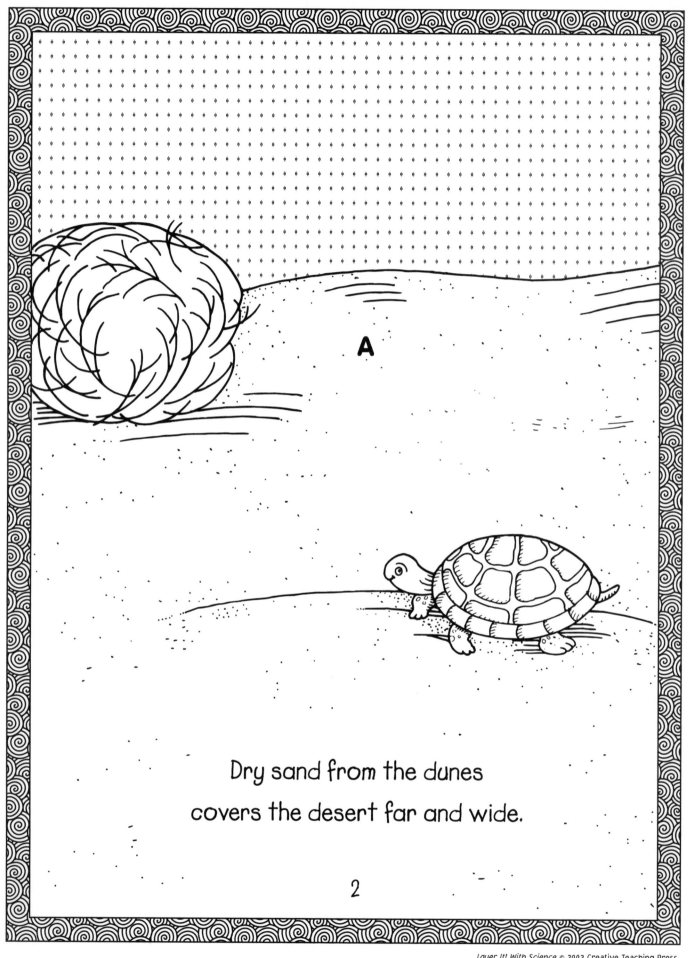

A

Dry sand from the dunes
covers the desert far and wide.

2

Layer It! With Science © 2002 Creative Teaching Press

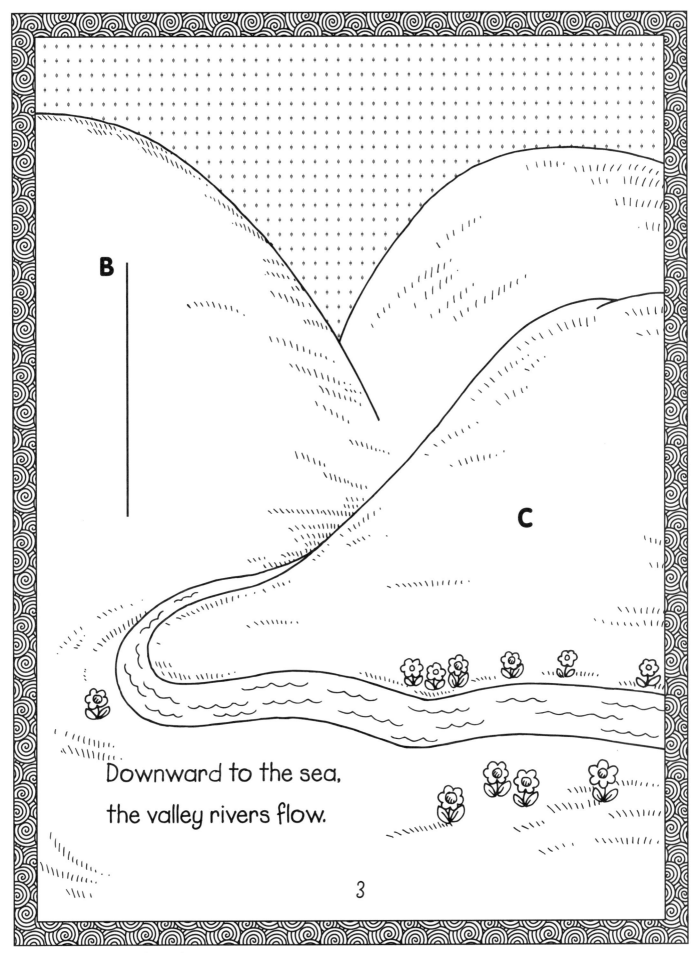

B

C

Downward to the sea,
the valley rivers flow.

3

Layer It! With Science © 2002 Creative Teaching Press

D

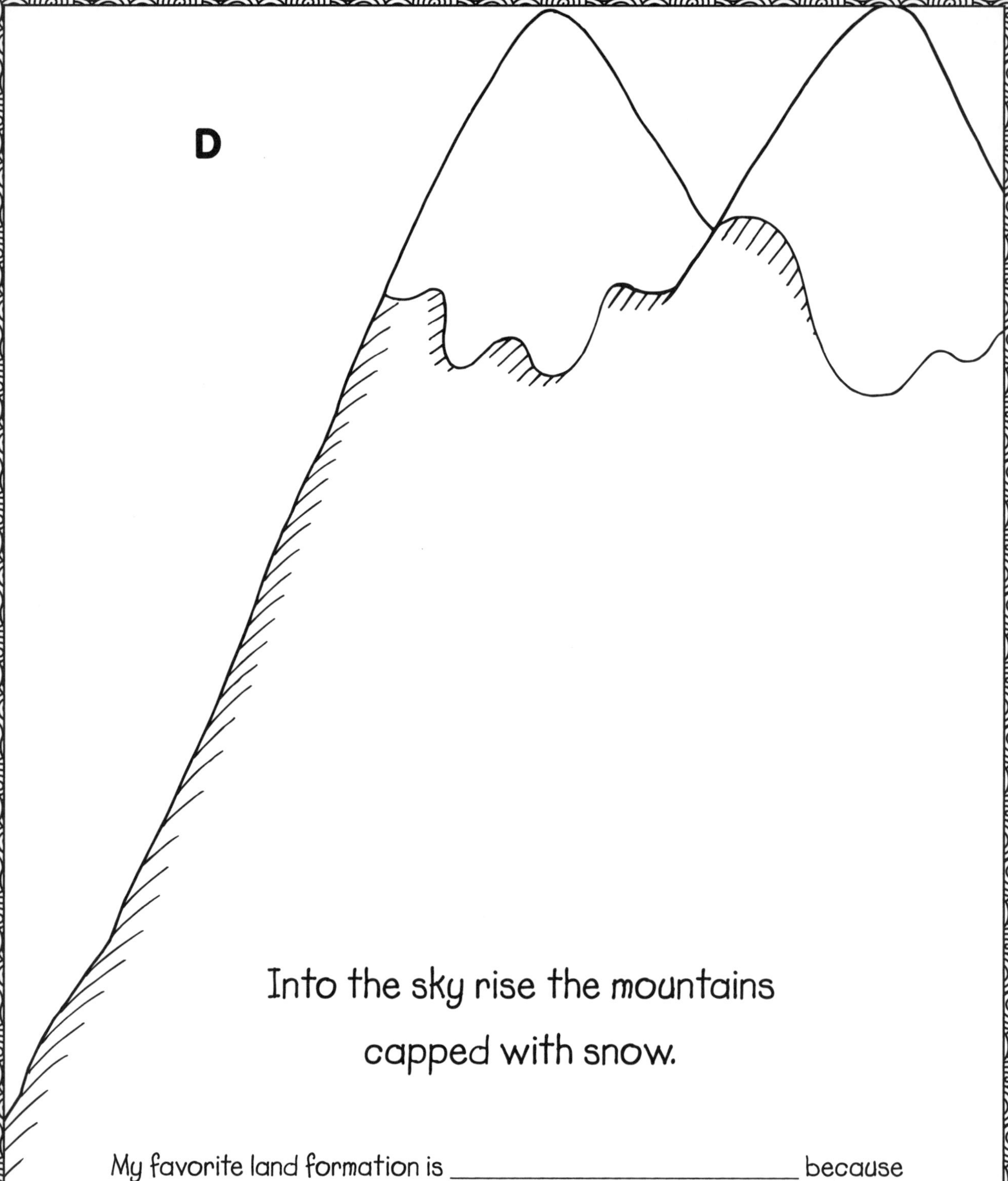

Into the sky rise the mountains
capped with snow.

My favorite land formation is _____ because

_____

_____

4

Layer It! With Science © 2002 Creative Teaching Press

The Life of a Flower

Materials

- ✂ Art Pieces reproducible (page 31) white
- ✂ Page One reproducible (page 32) light brown
- ✂ Page Two reproducible (page 33) brown
- ✂ Page Three reproducible (page 34) light green
- ✂ Page Four reproducible (page 35) light brown
- ✂ Page Five reproducible (page 36) light blue
- ✂ crayons or markers
- ✂ scissors
- ✂ X-ACTO® knife (optional) (for teacher use only)
- ✂ craft sticks
- ✂ glue
- ✂ translucent glitter
- ✂ flower seeds
- ✂ small fresh or dry leaves
- ✂ brass fasteners

Directions ●

Art Pieces Give each child an Art Pieces reproducible and an envelope. Have children color and cut out the four art pieces and place them inside their envelope. Tell children to place their envelope in their file folder. Collect each child's folder, and distribute it at the beginning of each day's activity.

Page One Cut a slit next to the letter A on each child's Page One reproducible. Give children their revised page and a craft stick. Have them remove the worms art piece from their envelope and glue it to the craft stick. Tell children to cut off the diamond pattern on the page and discard it. Ask them to color the remainder of the page and then slide the prepared craft stick through the slit.

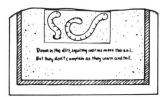

Page Two Give each child a Page Two reproducible, one flower seed, and translucent glitter. Have children remove the watering can art piece from their envelope and glue glitter to the water. Set aside the art pieces until the glue is dry. Tell children to cut off the diamond pattern on the page and discard it. Ask them to color the remainder of the page, glue the seed over the picture of a seed, and glue the watering can over the letter B.

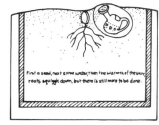

Page Three Give each child a Page Three reproducible. Have children remove the bee art piece from their envelope. Tell children to cut off the diamond pattern on the page and discard it. Ask them to color the remainder of the page and glue the bee over the letter C.

Page Four Give each child a Page Four reproducible and some fresh or dry leaves. Tell children to cut off the diamond pattern on the page and discard it. Ask them to color the remainder of the page and glue the leaves around the bottom of the page.

Page Five Give each child a Page Five reproducible and a brass fastener. Have children remove the life cycle art piece from their envelope. Ask children to color the page and place the brass fastener through the dot on the life cycle and the dot on the page (below the letter D). Invite them to turn the life cycle in the direction of the arrows to learn about the life cycle of a plant and then respond to the writing prompt.

Art Pieces

A

B

C

D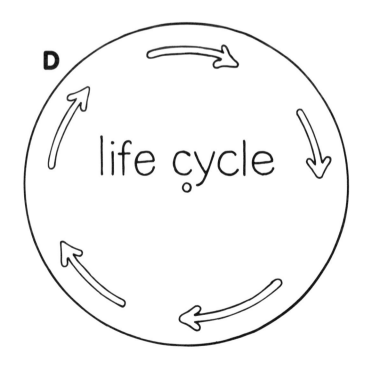

life cycle

Layer It! With Science © 2002 Creative Teaching Press

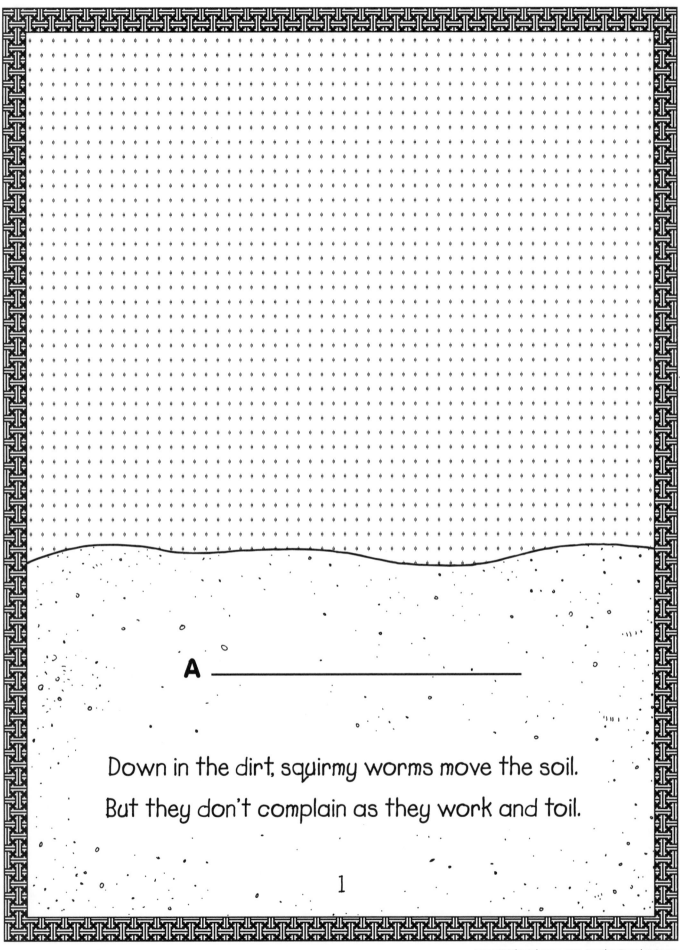

A _____

Down in the dirt, squirmy worms move the soil.

But they don't complain as they work and toil.

1

Layer It! With Science © 2002 Creative Teaching Press

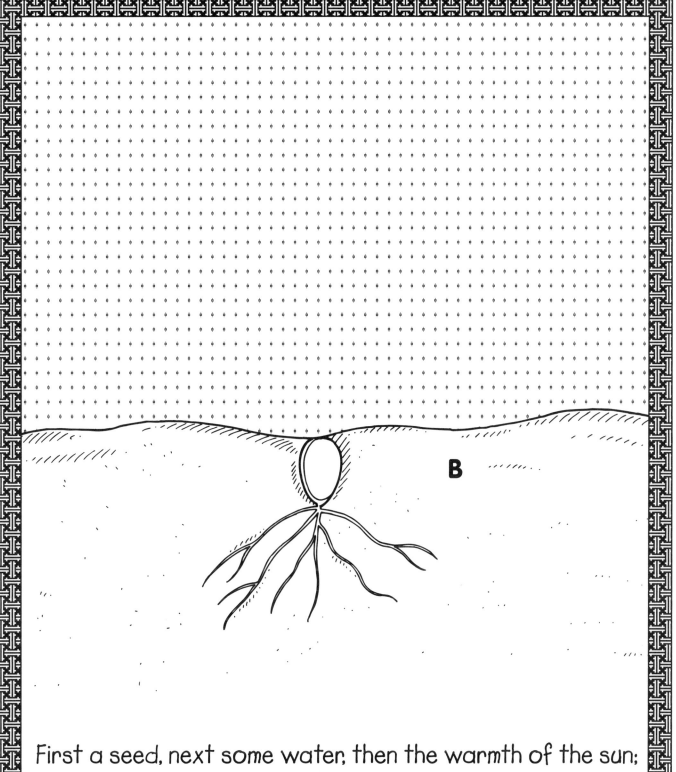

First a seed, next some water, then the warmth of the sun;
roots squiggle down, but there is still more to be done.

2

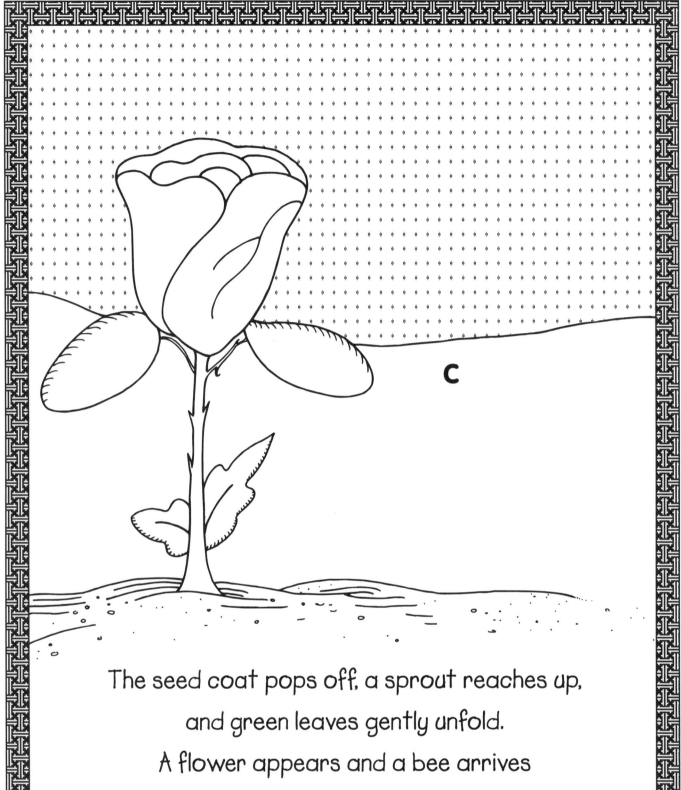

C

The seed coat pops off, a sprout reaches up,
and green leaves gently unfold.
A flower appears and a bee arrives
to gather pollen of gold.

3

Layer It! With Science © 2002 Creative Teaching Press

The flower withers and the seeds drop;
but don't be sad because . . .

4

Layer It! With Science © 2002 Creative Teaching Press

D
•

its beauty lives on in a brand-new flower

as the life cycle goes around again.

Explain the life cycle of a flower. _____

_____

_____

5

Layer It! With Science © 2002 Creative Teaching Press

Much about Matter

Materials

- ✂ Art Pieces reproducible (page 39) white
- ✂ Page One reproducible (page 40) light blue
- ✂ Page Two reproducible (page 41) light brown
- ✂ Page Three reproducible (page 42) yellow
- ✂ Page Four reproducible (page 43) light blue
- ✂ Page Five reproducible (page 44) light brown
- ✂ crayons or markers
- ✂ scissors
- ✂ X-ACTO® knife (optional) (for teacher use only)
- ✂ craft sticks
- ✂ glue
- ✂ blue glitter

Directions

Art Pieces Give each child an Art Pieces reproducible and an envelope. Have children color and cut out the seven art pieces and place them inside their envelope. Tell children to place their envelope in their file folder. Collect each child's folder, and distribute it at the beginning of each day's activity.

Page One Give each child a Page One reproducible. Tell children to cut off the diamond pattern on the page and discard it. Ask them to color the remainder of the page.

Page Two Cut a slit next to the letter A on each child's Page Two reproducible. Give children their revised page and a craft stick. Have children remove the bulldozer art piece from their envelope and glue it to the craft stick.

Tell them to cut off the diamond pattern on the page and discard it. Ask children to color the remainder of the page and then slide the prepared craft stick through the slit.

Page Three Cut a slit next to the letter B on each child's Page Three reproducible. Give children their revised page, a craft stick, and blue glitter. Have them remove the elephant and clown art pieces from their envelope and

glue the elephant to the craft stick. Tell children to cut off the diamond pattern on the page and discard it. Have them glue glitter on the pool to resemble water. Set aside the pages until the glue is dry. Ask children to color the remainder of the page, glue the clown over the letter C, and slide the prepared craft stick through the slit.

Page Four Cut a slit next to the letter D on each child's Page Four reproducible. Give children their revised page and a craft stick. Have children remove the evaporated water art piece from their envelope and glue it to the craft stick. Tell them to cut off the diamond pattern on the page and discard it. Ask children to color the remainder of the page and then slide the prepared craft stick through the slit.

Gas is without body —
invisible to the eye.
It's sometimes hard to know it is there —
just don't ask me why!

Page Five Give each child a Page Five reproducible. Have children remove the water vapors, container, and ice cube art pieces from their envelope. Ask them to color the page and glue the water vapors over the letter E, the container over the letter F, and the ice cube over the letter G. Invite children to respond to the writing prompt.

Gas

Liquid

Solid

Whether matter is a solid or a liquid or a gas —
it has weight that you can measure,
so we say it has mass.

We also know: its shape
can change.

Art Pieces

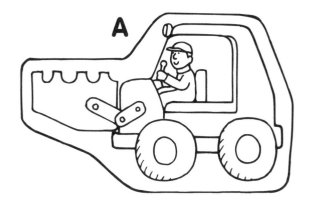

A

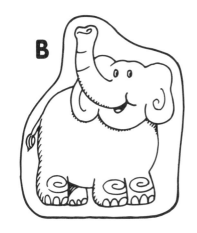

B

C

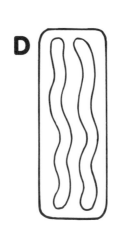

D

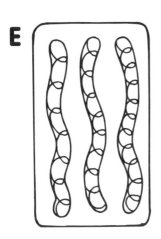

E

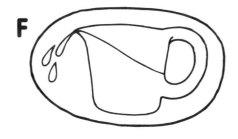

F

G

The world is made of matter.

That is a fact.

Everything is something,

if you want to be exact.

1

Layer It! With Science © 2002 Creative Teaching Press

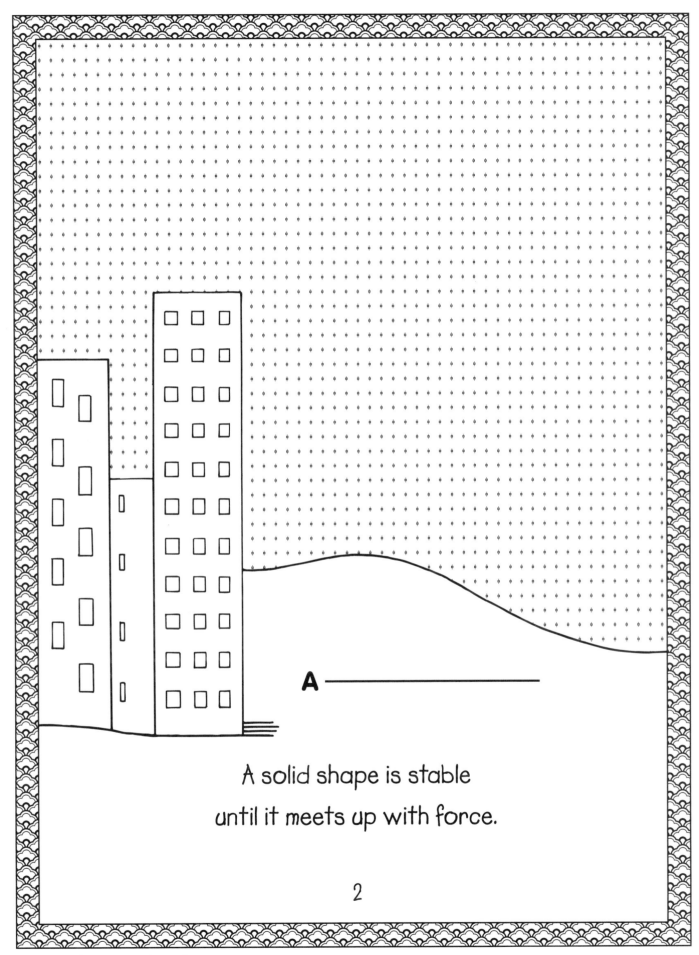

A ———————————————

A solid shape is stable
until it meets up with force.

2

Layer It! With Science © 2002 Creative Teaching Press

B

C

A liquid's shape is formed
by its container, of course.

3

Layer It! With Science © 2002 Creative Teaching Press

D

Gas is without body—

invisible to the eye.

It's sometimes hard to know it is there—

just don't ask me why!

4

Layer It! With Science © 2002 Creative Teaching Press

Gas

F

E

Liquid

Solid

G

Whether matter is a solid or a liquid or a gas—
it has weight that you can measure,
so we say it has mass.

Water is a liquid because _____

_____

_____

5

Layer It! With Science © 2002 Creative Teaching Press

The Rain Forest

Materials

- ✂ Art Pieces reproducible (page 46) white
- ✂ Page One reproducible (page 47) light brown
- ✂ Page Two reproducible (page 48) brown
- ✂ Page Three reproducible (page 49) light green
- ✂ Page Four reproducible (page 50) light blue
- ✂ crayons or markers
- ✂ scissors
- ✂ glue
- ✂ X-ACTO® knife (optional) (for teacher use only)
- ✂ craft sticks

Directions •

Art Pieces Give each child an Art Pieces reproducible and an envelope. Have children color and cut out the eight art pieces and place them inside their envelope. Tell children to place their envelope in their file folder. Collect each child's folder, and distribute it at the beginning of each day's activity.

Page One Give each child a Page One reproducible. Have children remove the iguana art piece from their envelope. Tell children to cut off the diamond pattern on the page and discard it. Ask them to color the remainder of the page and glue the iguana over the letter A.

Page Two Cut a slit next to the letter C on each child's Page Two reproducible. Give children their revised page and a craft stick. Have children remove the tarantula and margay art pieces from their envelope and glue the margay to the craft stick. Tell them to cut off the diamond pattern on the page and discard it. Ask children to color the remainder of the page, glue the tarantula over the letter B,

and slide the prepared craft stick through the slit.

Page Three Cut a slit next to the letter E on each child's Page Three reproducible. Give children their revised page and a craft stick. Have them remove the monkeys, sloth, and kinkajou art pieces from their envelope and glue the sloth to the craft stick. Tell children to cut off the diamond pattern on the page and discard it. Ask them to color the remainder of the page, glue the monkeys over the letter D and the kinkajou over the letter F, and then slide the prepared craft stick through the slit.

Page Four Give each child a Page Four reproducible. Have children remove the parrots and eagle art pieces from their envelope. Ask them to color the page and glue the parrots over the letter G and the eagle over the letter H. Invite children to respond to the writing prompt.

Art Pieces

A
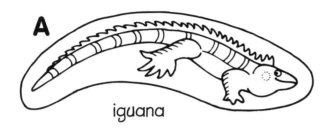
iguana

B
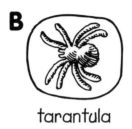
tarantula

C
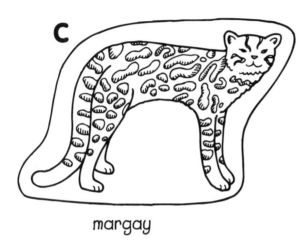
margay

D

monkeys

E
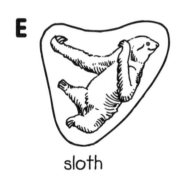
sloth

F

kinkajou

G

parrots

H

eagle

Layer It! With Science © 2002 Creative Teaching Press

On the rain forest floor,
quietly look around.
Plants and animals
are easily found.

A

1

Layer It! With Science © 2002 Creative Teaching Press

C ————————

This tarantula lives in the understory.

The ocelot and margay do, too.

Butterflies flitter from here to there,

teasing the kinkajou.

B

2

Layer It! With Science © 2002 Creative Teaching Press

High in the branches of the canopy,
monkeys chitter and chatter.
They all seem to enjoy the view,
but to the sloth only sleep will matter.

3

Layer It! With Science © 2002 Creative Teaching Press

G   H

Way up high in the emergent layer,
plants reach for the light.
Parrots and eagles fly above
and make a glorious sight!

The rain forest has _____

_____

_____

4

Layer It! With Science © 2002 Creative Teaching Press

The Sea of Life

Materials

- ✂ Art Pieces reproducible (page 53) white
- ✂ Page One reproducible (page 54) light blue
- ✂ Page Two reproducible (page 55) light blue
- ✂ Page Three reproducible (page 56) blue
- ✂ Page Four reproducible (page 57) white
- ✂ Page Five reproducible (page 58) white
- ✂ crayons or markers
- ✂ scissors
- ✂ glue
- ✂ X-ACTO® knife (optional) (for teacher use only)
- ✂ craft sticks

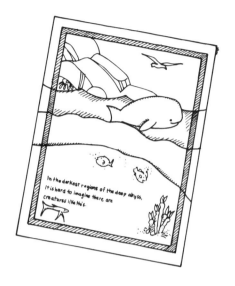

Directions ●

Art Pieces Give each child an Art Pieces reproducible and an envelope. Have children color and cut out the ten art pieces and place them inside their envelope. Tell children to place their envelope in their file folder. Collect each child's folder, and distribute it at the beginning of each day's activity.

Page One Give each child a Page One reproducible. Have children remove the hatchet fish and football fish art pieces from their envelope. Tell children to cut off the diamond pattern on the page and discard it. Ask them to color the remainder of the page and glue the hatchet fish over the letter A and the football fish over the letter B.

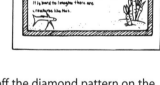

Page Two Give each child a Page Two reproducible. Have children remove the octopus and lobster art pieces from their envelope. Tell children to cut off the diamond pattern on the page and discard it. Ask them to color the remainder of the page and glue the octopus over the letter C and the lobster over the letter D.

Page Three Cut a slit next to the letter E on each child's Page Three reproducible. Give children their revised page and a craft stick. Have them remove the whale and marlin art pieces from their envelope and glue the whale to the craft stick. Tell children to cut off the diamond pattern on the page and discard it. Ask them to color the remainder of the page, glue the marlin over the letter F, and then slide the prepared craft stick through the slit.

Page Four

Give each child a Page Four reproducible.

Have children remove the sea star, sand crab, and two cover art pieces from their envelope. Tell children to cut off the diamond pattern on the page and discard it. Ask them to color the remainder of the page and glue the sea star over the letter G and

the sand crab over the letter H. Have children glue the top edge of the covers over the letters I and J (along the top edge of the sea caves).

Page Five

Give each child a Page Five reproducible.

Ask children to color the page. Invite them to respond to the writing prompt.

Art Pieces

A

hatchet fish

B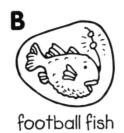

football fish

C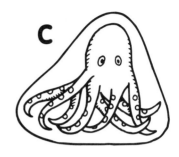

D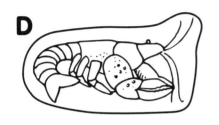

E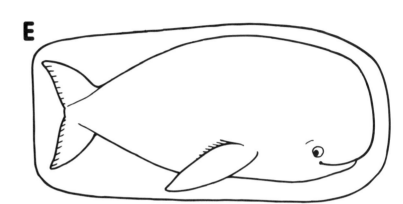

F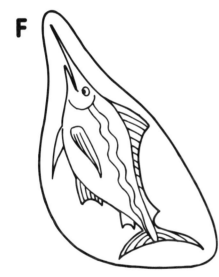

G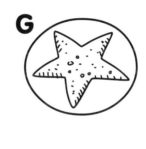

H

I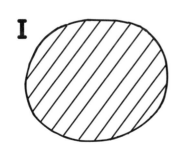

J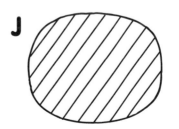

In the darkest regions of the deep abyss,
it is hard to imagine there are
creatures like this.

1

Layer It! With Science © 2002 Creative Teaching Press

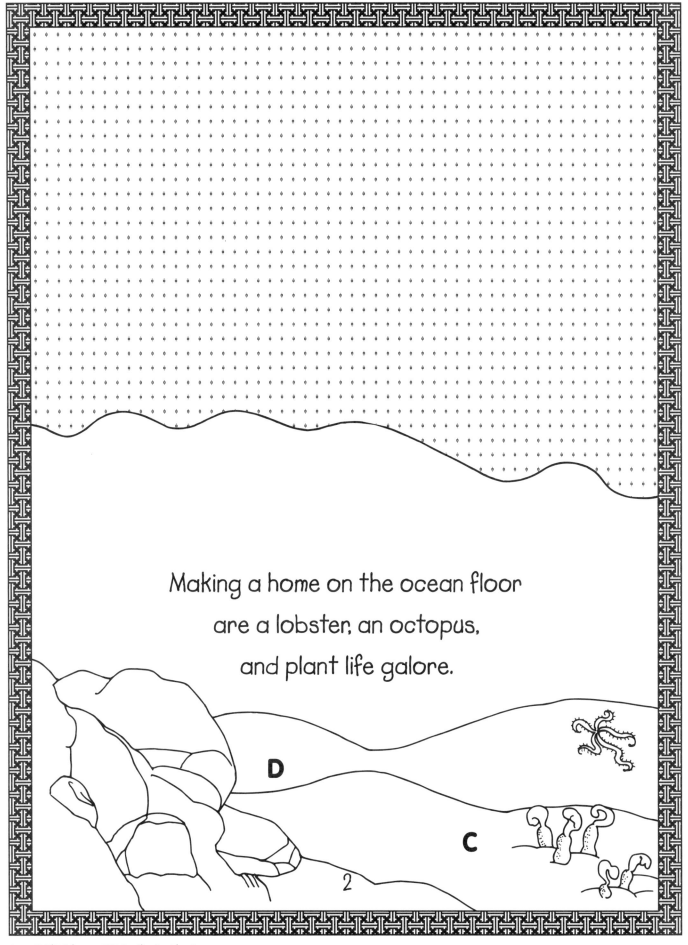

Making a home on the ocean floor
are a lobster, an octopus,
and plant life galore.

D

C

2

Layer It! With Science © 2002 Creative Teaching Press

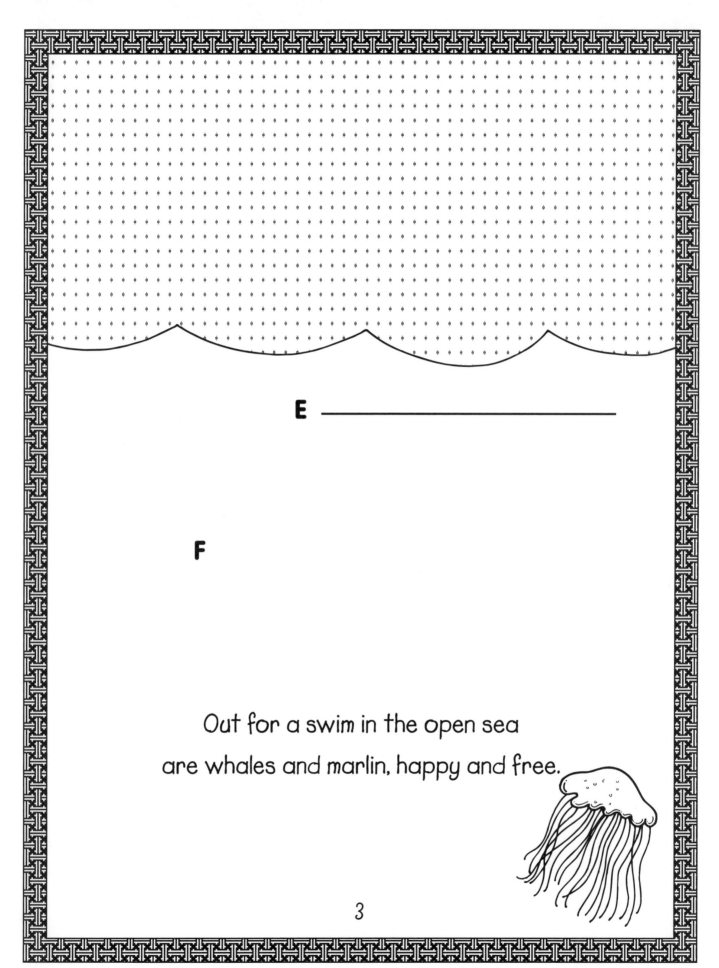

E _____

F

Out for a swim in the open sea
are whales and marlin, happy and free.

3

Layer It! With Science © 2002 Creative Teaching Press

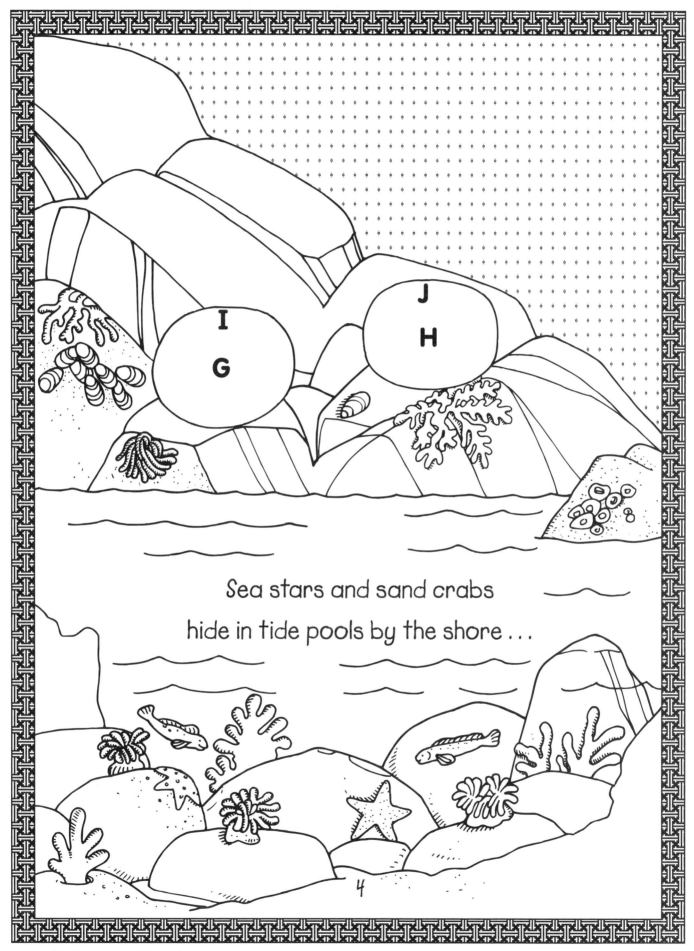

Sea stars and sand crabs
hide in tide pools by the shore . . .

Layer It! With Science © 2002 Creative Teaching Press

Below the place where
the seagulls soar.

Something I want to learn about the sea is _____

_____

_____

5

Layer It! With Science © 2002 Creative Teaching Press

There's No Place Like Home

Materials

- ✂ Art Pieces reproducible (page 60) white
- ✂ Page One reproducible (page 61) blue
- ✂ Page Two reproducible (page 62) brown
- ✂ Page Three reproducible (page 63) light green
- ✂ Page Four reproducible (page 64) light blue
- ✂ crayons or markers
- ✂ scissors
- ✂ X-ACTO® knife (optional) (for teacher use only)
- ✂ craft sticks
- ✂ glue
- ✂ cotton balls

Directions •

Art Pieces Give each child an Art Pieces reproducible and an envelope. Have children color and cut out the six art pieces and place them inside their envelope. Tell children to place their envelope in their file folder. Collect each child's folder, and distribute it at the beginning of each day's activity.

Page One Cut a slit next to the letter A on each child's Page One reproducible. Give children their revised page and a craft stick. Have them

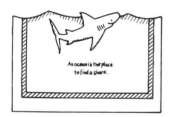

remove the shark art piece from their envelope and glue it to the craft stick. Tell children to cut off the diamond pattern on the page and discard it. Have them slide the prepared craft stick through the slit.

Page Two Give each child a Page Two reproducible. Have children remove the rabbit art piece from their envelope. Tell children to cut off the diamond pattern on

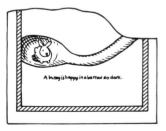

the page and discard it. Ask them to color the remainder of the page and glue the rabbit over the letter B.

Page Three Give each child a Page Three reproducible. Have children remove the fox and cover art pieces from their envelope. Tell children to cut off the diamond pattern on the page and discard it. Ask them to color the remainder of the page and

glue the fox over the letter C. Have children glue the top edge of the cover over the letter D (along the top edge of the den).

Page Four Cut a slit next to the letter E on each child's Page Four reproducible. Give children their revised page, a craft stick, and two cotton balls. Have children remove the eagle and cloud art pieces from their envelope and glue the eagle to the craft stick. Have them tear their cotton

balls into small pieces and glue the pieces over the cloud. Set aside the art pieces until the glue is dry. Ask children to color the page, glue the cloud over the letter F, and slide the prepared craft stick through the slit. Invite them to respond to the writing prompt.

Art Pieces

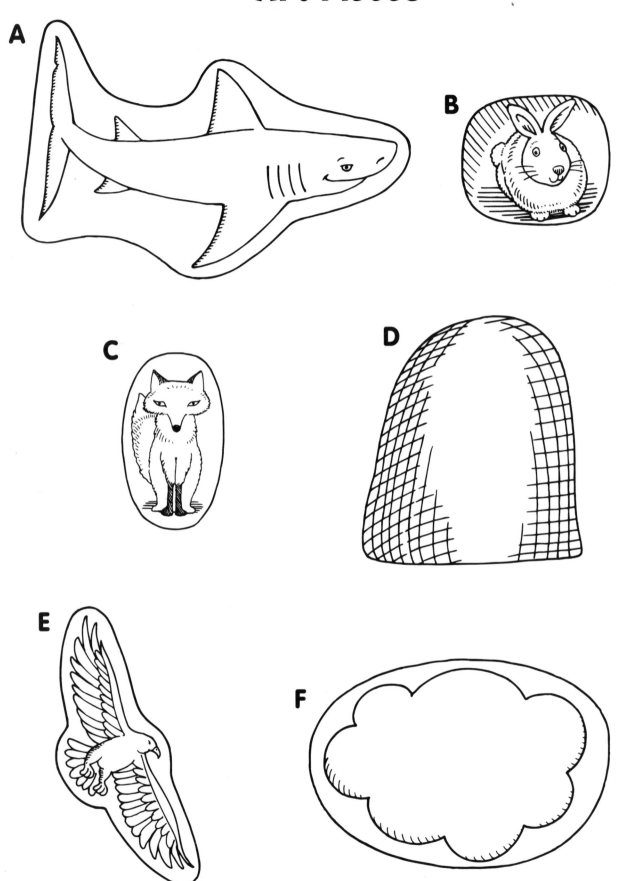

A

B

C

D

E

F

There's No Place Like Home

Layer It! With Science © 2002 Creative Teaching Press

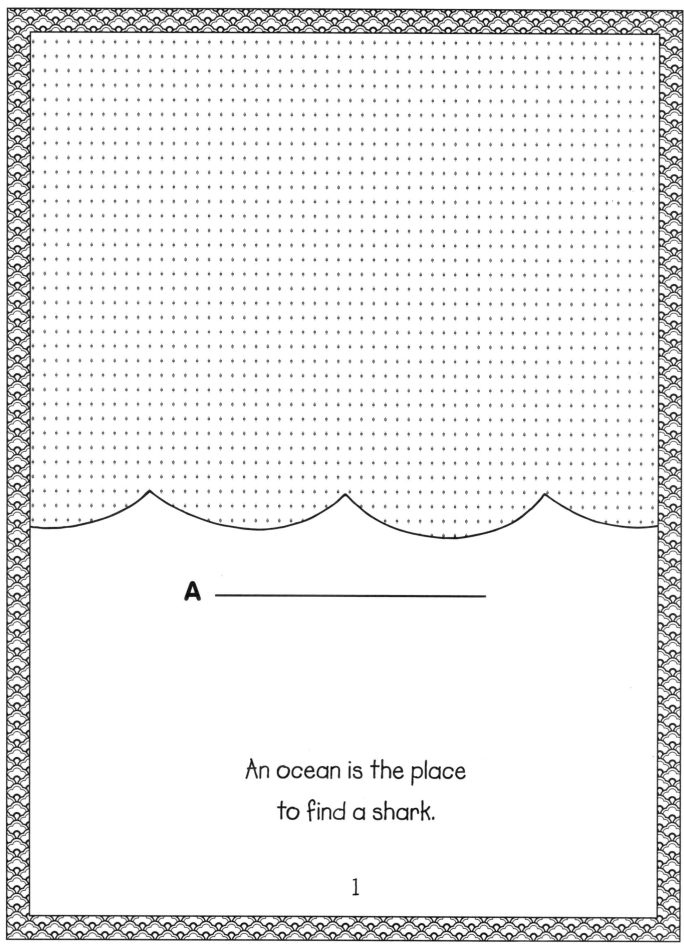

A _____

An ocean is the place
to find a shark.

1

Layer It! With Science © 2002 Creative Teaching Press

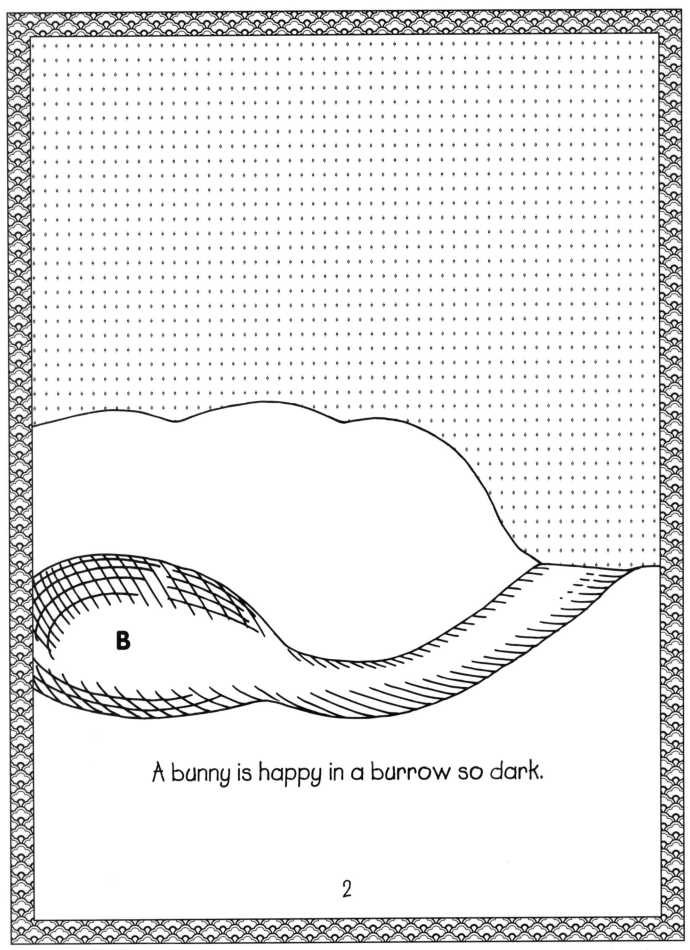

B

A bunny is happy in a burrow so dark.

2

Layer It! With Science © 2002 Creative Teaching Press

There's No Place Like Home

A cozy den is just right
for a fox.

3

Layer It! With Science © 2002 Creative Teaching Press

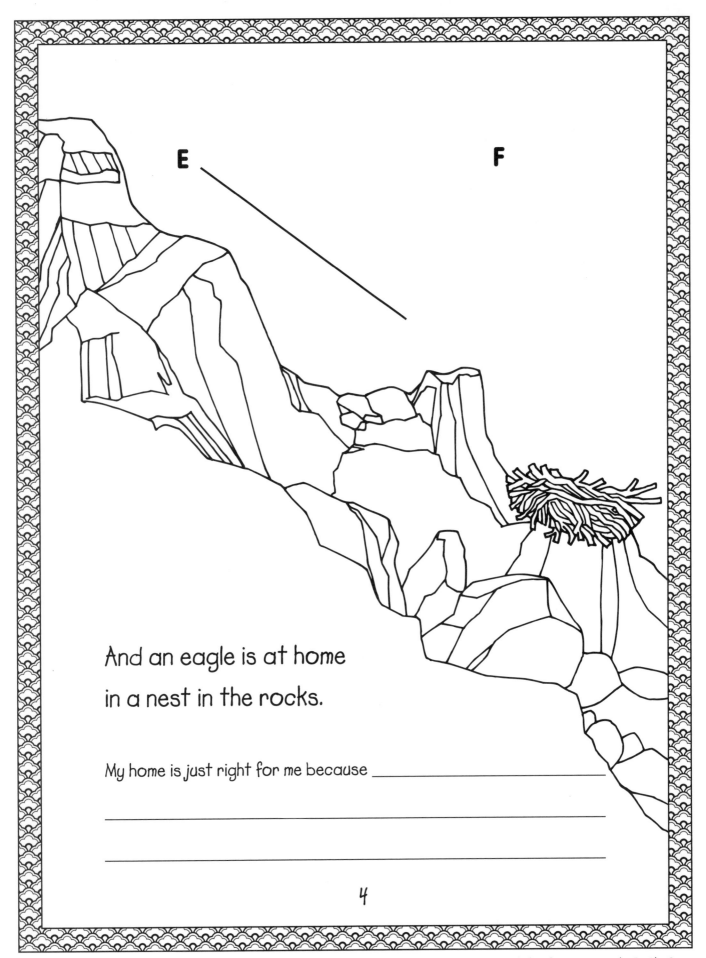

E

F

And an eagle is at home
in a nest in the rocks.

My home is just right for me because _____

_____

_____

4

Layer It! With Science © 2002 Creative Teaching Press

The Water Cycle

Materials

- ✂ Art Pieces reproducible (page 67) white
- ✂ Page One reproducible (page 68) blue
- ✂ Page Two reproducible (page 69) light brown
- ✂ Page Three reproducible (page 70) white
- ✂ Page Four reproducible (page 71) light blue
- ✂ Page Five reproducible (page 72) blue
- ✂ crayons or markers
- ✂ scissors
- ✂ gold, translucent, and blue glitter
- ✂ glue
- ✂ cotton balls
- ✂ X-ACTO® knife (optional) (for teacher use only)
- ✂ craft sticks

Directions ●

Art Pieces Give each child an Art Pieces reproducible and an envelope. Have children color and cut out the five art pieces and place them inside their envelope. Tell children to place their envelope in their file folder. Collect each child's folder, and distribute it at the beginning of each day's activity.

Page One Give each child a Page One reproducible and gold glitter. Tell children to cut off the diamond pattern on the page and discard it. Ask them to color the remainder of the page and glue glitter on the lightning bolt. Set aside the pages until the glue is dry.

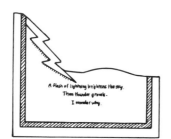

Page Two Give each child a Page Two reproducible, blue and translucent glitter, and three cotton balls. Have children remove the rainbow art piece from their envelope and glue translucent glitter on it. Set aside the art pieces until the glue is dry. Tell children to cut off the diamond pattern on the page and discard it. Ask them to color the remainder of the page, glue the rainbow over the letter A (making sure the rainbow touches the cloud). Have children tear their cotton balls into small pieces and glue the pieces over the cloud. Have children glue blue glitter on the raindrops and puddle to resemble water. Set aside the pages until the glue is dry.

Page Three Give each child a Page Three reproducible and blue and translucent glitter. Tell children to cut off the diamond pattern on the page and discard it. Ask them to color the remainder of the page, glue blue glitter on the river to resemble water, and glue translucent glitter on the mountain peaks to resemble snow. Set aside the pages until the glue is dry.

Page Four

Cut a slit next to the letter B on each child's Page Four reproducible. Give children their revised page and a craft stick. Have them remove the evaporation art piece from their envelope and glue it to the craft stick. Tell children to cut off the diamond pattern on the page and discard it. Ask them to color the remainder of the page and then slide the prepared craft stick through the slit.

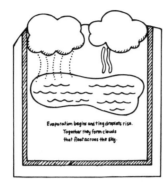

Evaporation begins and tiny droplets rise.
Together they form clouds
that float across the sky.

Page Five

Give each child a Page Five reproducible, translucent and blue glitter, and one cotton ball. Have children remove the evaporation, condensation, and precipitation art pieces from their envelope. Ask them to glue translucent glitter on the evaporation piece, the cotton ball on the condensation piece, and blue glitter on the raindrops of the precipitation piece. Set aside the art pieces until the glue is dry. Have children glue the evaporation piece over the letter C, the condensation piece over the letter D, and the precipitation piece over the letter E. Invite them to respond to the writing prompt.

water cycle

Heavy with moisture,
the clouds drop water
as snow or rain,
and the water cycle begins once again

We need water to drink and
make plants grow.

Art Pieces

A

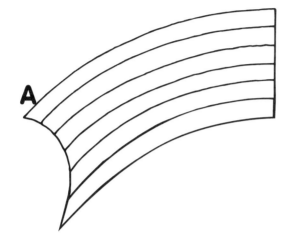

B

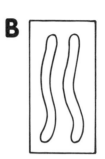

C

evaporation

D

condensation

E

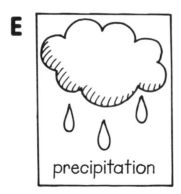

precipitation

A flash of lightning brightens the sky.

Then thunder growls—

I wonder why.

1

Layer It! With Science © 2002 Creative Teaching Press

A

Rain makes puddles on the ground.

A rainbow appears without a sound.

2

Layer It! With Science © 2002 Creative Teaching Press

The heat of the sun melts

the cold mountain snow.

It makes a river—

and then to the sea it will flow.

3

Layer It! With Science © 2002 Creative Teaching Press

Evaporation begins and tiny droplets rise.
Together they form clouds
that float across the sky.

4

Layer It! With Science © 2002 Creative Teaching Press

D

C 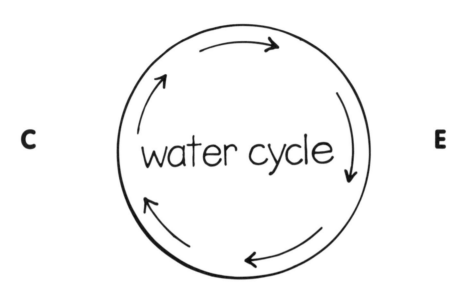 **E**

Heavy with moisture,

the clouds drop water

as snow or rain,

and the water cycle begins once again.

The water cycle is important because _____

_____

_____

5

Layer It! With Science © 2002 Creative Teaching Press

Weather Watch

Materials

- ✂ Art Pieces reproducible (page 75) white
- ✂ Page One reproducible (page 76) light blue
- ✂ Page Two reproducible (page 77) blue
- ✂ Page Three reproducible (page 78) yellow
- ✂ Page Four reproducible (page 79) light brown
- ✂ Page Five reproducible (page 80) white
- ✂ crayons or markers
- ✂ scissors
- ✂ translucent, blue, and gold glitter
- ✂ glue
- ✂ cotton balls
- ✂ X-ACTO® knife (optional) (for teacher use only)
- ✂ craft sticks

Directions •

Art Pieces Give each child an Art Pieces reproducible and an envelope. Have children color and cut out the five art pieces and place them inside their envelope. Tell children to place their envelope in their file folder. Collect each child's folder, and distribute it at the beginning of each day's activity.

Page One Give each child a Page One reproducible and translucent glitter. Have children remove the sun art piece from their envelope. Tell children to cut off the diamond pattern on the page and discard it. Ask them to color the remainder of the page, glue the sun over the letter A, and glue glitter on the mountain peak to resemble snow. Set aside the pages until the glue is dry.

Page Two Cut a slit next to the letter B on each child's Page Two reproducible. Give children their revised page, a craft stick, and blue glitter. Have children remove the raindrops and thunder cloud art pieces from their envelope. Invite them to glue the raindrops to the craft stick and then glue glitter on the raindrops. Set aside the art pieces until the glue is dry. Tell children to cut off the

diamond pattern on the page and discard it. Ask them to color the remainder of page, glue the thunder cloud over the letter C, and then slide the prepared craft stick through the slit.

Page Three Give each child a Page Three reproducible and gold glitter. Have children remove the lightning bolt art piece from their envelope. Tell children to cut off the diamond pattern on the page and discard it. Have them glue glitter on the lighting bolt. Set aside the art pieces until the glue is dry. Ask children to color the remainder of the page and glue the lightning bolt over the letter D.

Page Four Give each child a Page Four reproducible, translucent glitter, and two cotton balls. Have children remove the snowflakes art piece from their envelope. Tell children to cut off the diamond pattern on the page and discard it. Ask

them to color the remainder of the page and glue the snowflakes over the letter E. Have children glue glitter on the mountain peaks to resemble snow. Have them tear the cotton balls into small pieces and glue the pieces over the clouds. Set aside the pages until the glue is dry.

Page Five Give each child a Page Five reproducible and translucent glitter. Invite children to respond to the writing prompt. Ask them to color the page and then glue glitter around the page to resemble snow. Set aside the pages until the glue is dry.

Art Pieces

A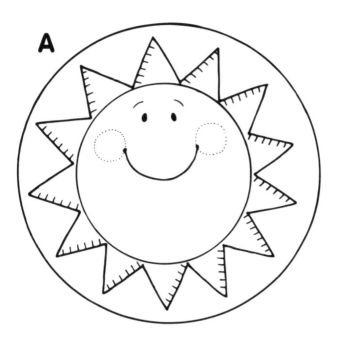

B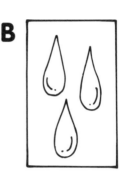

C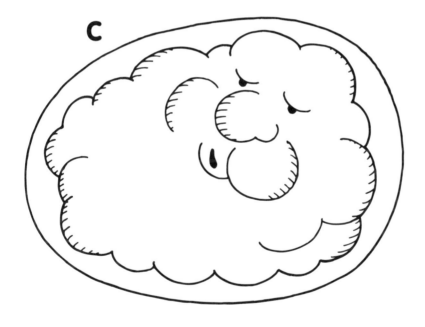

D

E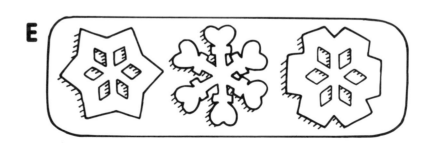

A

I feel sunshine and wind.

1

Layer It! With Science © 2002 Creative Teaching Press

B

C

I hear thunder and rain.

2

Layer It! With Science © 2002 Creative Teaching Press

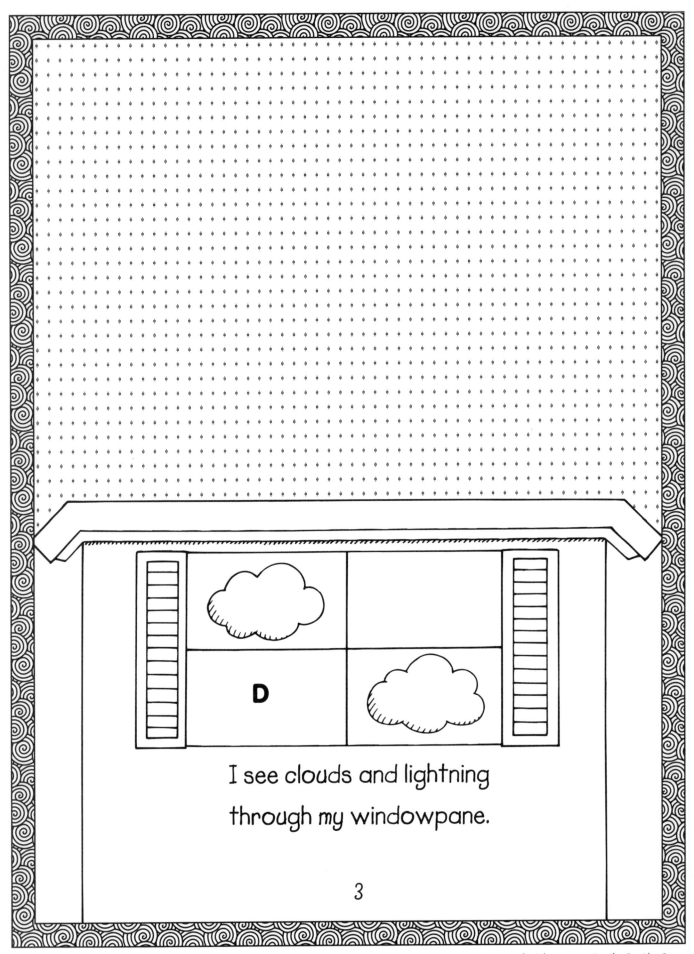

I see clouds and lightning

through my windowpane.

3

Layer It! With Science © 2002 Creative Teaching Press

E

All of these things alone or together . . .

4

Layer It! With Science © 2002 Creative Teaching Press

Make up something that we call—WEATHER!

The type of weather I like most is _____ because

_____

_____

5

Layer It! With Science © 2002 Creative Teaching Press